Monsieur Roscoe

On Holiday

Jim Field

At the very top of a very tall building lives
a friendly dog called Monsieur Roscoe.

Bonjour Monsieur Roscoe!

Today is a special day. Monsieur Roscoe and his goldfish, Fry, are going on holiday to visit their friends.

Bonjour je m'appelle Monsieur Roscoe.
Hello, my name is Mr Roscoe.

It's time to pack. There are lots of things to remember.
Don't forget your toothbrush, Monsieur Roscoe!

un pantalon
trousers

un short
shorts

un T-shirt
T-shirt

une chemise
shirt

des chaussettes
socks

des lunettes de soleil
sunglasses

un nounours
teddy bear

des chaussures
shoes

un parapluie
umbrella

un slip
underpants

SNAX

At last, Monsieur Roscoe and Fry are ready to leave.
Happy holidays, Monsieur Roscoe!

RESTAURANT

CINÉMA

CAFÉ

un taxi
taxi

un camion poubelle
dustcart

un bus
bus

une moto
motorbike

une voiture
car

un vélo
bike

une ambulance
ambulance

The city
is big and the
streets are very busy.
*Hurry up, Monsieur Roscoe,
or you'll miss your train!*

ÉPICERIE

COIFFEUR

BOULANGERIE

BOULANGERI

OUVRE

PÂTISSERIE

un fourgon
postal
mail van

un scooter
scooter

une voiture de police
police car

Monsieur Roscoe and Fry catch the train, just in time.
Phew! That was close!

The train goes into the tunnel . . .

. . . and comes out into the countryside.

Monsieur Roscoe and Fry are going camping with their friend, Eva.
Oh no, it's starting to rain!

Il pleut !
It's raining!

Viens vite !
Come quickly!

Monsieur Roscoe has brought his camping gear, but – oh dear! – he doesn't know how to put up a tent.

une clôture
fence

un camping car
campervan

une ombre
shadow

dormir
sleep

une tente
tent

un feu de camp
campfire

une bûche
log

la lune
moon

une lampe
torche
torch

une caravane
caravan

un buisson
bush

un barbecue
barbecue

une table de pique-nique
picnic table

des bottes
boots

Luckily, Eva can help.
Where's your teddy, Monsieur Roscoe?

After a night under the stars, it's time to say *au revoir*.

Soon Monsieur Roscoe and Fry are on a bus,
travelling up into the snowy mountains.

They catch a lift to the very top of the ski slopes.

Monsieur Roscoe is looking
for his friend, Stan.

J'arrive !
I'm coming!

Bonjour Stan !
Hello, Stan!

There he is,
skiing down the mountain.
Hang on tight, Monsieur Roscoe!

It's a long way down from the top of the mountain . . .
Oh crumbs, Monsieur Roscoe, that's the ski jump!

un bonhomme de neige
snowman

une boule de neige
snowball

un snowboard
snowboard

la neige
snow

une luge
sledge

des patins à glace
ice skate

un bonnet
hat

la montagne
mountain

des skis
skis

un télésiège
chair lift

**des bâtons
de ski**
ski poles

des gants
gloves

**un saut
à ski**
ski jump

10 10 10 10

Wowee!
Stan and the crowd
are very impressed!

Stan would like to take Monsieur Roscoe snowboarding.
But it's time to move on. *Next time, Monsieur Roscoe.*

It's hard work cycling to the lake.

Time for a rest, Monsieur Roscoe?

Monsieur Roscoe and Fry are glad to see their friend, Caro. She is going to take them for a trip in her boat!

la forêt
wood/forest

la colline
hill

un voilier
sailing boat

une péniche
houseboat

un bateau de pêche
fishing boat

une barque
rowing boat

un canoë
canoe

le lac
lake

le paddle
paddle board

un radeau
raft

la planche à voile
windsurfing

le ski nautique
waterski

une gondole
gondola

un bateau à moteur
motorboat

Monsieur Roscoe wants to have a go at steering. But it isn't as easy at it looks . . .
Watch out, Monsieur Roscoe!

All too soon, it's time to go. Caro helps them find
a big boat to take them on their way . . .

The next stop is Monsieur Roscoe's favourite place . . .

. . . the seaside!

Monsieur Roscoe can't wait to go swimming
with his friends, Jojo and Didi.

J'adore la mer !
I love the seaside!

Viens jouer !
Come and play!

*Don't forget your goggles,
Monsieur Roscoe!*

Monsieur Roscoe loves splashing in the sea.
Everyone is very impressed by his rubber ring!

un sauveteur
lifeguard

un cerf-volant
kite

un maillot de bain
swimming costume

une serviette
towel

un parasol
parasol

la plage
beach

la crème solaire
sun cream

un château de sable
sandcastle

surf
surf

la mer
sea

des vagues
waves

une bouée
rubber ring

des raquettes
rackets

Monsieur Roscoe and Fry have had a wonderful time at the beach, but there is still one more friend to visit.

They take a taxi to a pretty little village.

Look where you're going, Monsieur Roscoe!

Is that your tummy rumbling, Monsieur Roscoe?

Maybe their old friend Dougal knows a good café.

Monsieur Roscoe and Dougal order TWO
ice creams each, and a big fruity drink for Fry.

du pain
bread

de l'eau
water

un café
coffee

une salade
salad

un jus
juice

une glace
ice cream

un burger
burger

des olives
olives

du fromage
cheese

une chaise
chair

un gâteau
cake

des frites
French fries

une table
table

des bananes
bananas

This is the life, Monsieur Roscoe!

What a wonderful holiday! But now, it's time to go home.

Monsieur Roscoe and Fry have had great fun
with all of their friends.

Don't worry, Monsieur Roscoe, you'll see them again soon.

After a long journey, Monsieur Roscoe and
Fry make it back home to the city.

Bonne nuit everybody.

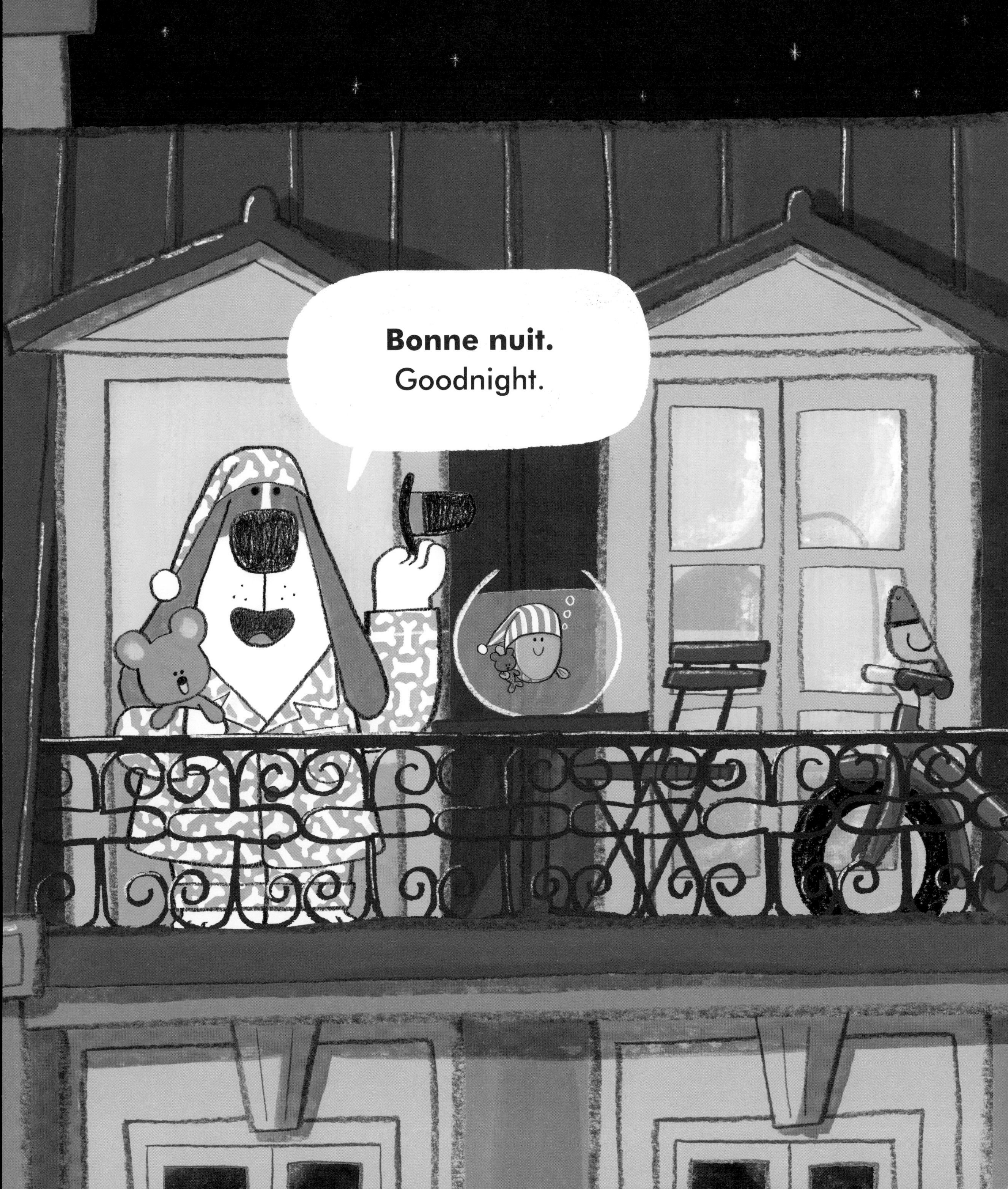

Monsieur Roscoe and Fry hope you've had fun with them on holiday. Can you spot the following items in the book?

IN THE CITY
- **orange car**
  une voiture orange
- **hairdresser**
  un coiffeur
- **pigeon**
  un pigeon

ON THE SLOPES
- **tiger**
  un tigre
- **6 yellow ducklings**
  6 canetons jaunes
- **zebra**
  un zèbre

AT THE BEACH
- **beachball**
  un ballon de plage
- **surfer**
  un surfeur
- **6 crabs**
  6 crabes

ON THE CAMPSITE
- **pink tent**
  une tente rose
- **guitar**
  une guitare
- **bird**
  un oiseau

ON THE LAKE
- **2 fishermen**
  2 pêcheurs
- **4 fish**
  4 poissons
- **mouse**
  une souris

AT THE CAFÉ
- **baby leopard**
  un bébé léopard
- **pizza**
  une pizza
- **hen**
  une poule

HODDER CHILDREN'S BOOKS
First published in Great Britain in 2020 by Hodder and Stoughton

Copyright © Jim Field 2020

The moral rights of the author-illustrator have been asserted.
All rights reserved

A CIP catalogue record for this book is available from the British Library.

ISBN: 978 1 444 93267 6

3 5 7 9 10 8 6 4 2

Printed and bound in China

FSC MIX Paper from responsible sources FSC® C104740

Hodder Children's Books
An imprint of Hachette Children's Group
Part of Hodder and Stoughton
Carmelite House, 50 Victoria Embankment,
London, EC4Y 0DZ
An Hachette UK Company

www.hachette.co.uk
www.hachettechildrens.co.uk

Hodder Children's Books

To 'mon amour' Sandy. Thanks to your ideas, patience, support, encouragement and French! Without you, this book would never have existed. Merci beaucoup ma chérie!